You can start feeling better about 10 minutes from now

Like loads of people, you're not feeling great at the moment.

Your system's a bit sluggish. You're miserable some of the time. You think your life could be better all round, but nothing seems to cheer you up these days.

So here's the good news: you can start to feel better in a few minutes from now. All you have to do is finish reading this book and then make some small, easy changes to what you do each day.

3

More good stuff

DON'T PANIC!

No broccoli is involved

You *will* have to get off the couch and walk about a bit. You'll also have to say no to a burger or two, but you won't have to wear Lycra shorts and we promise not to turn you into a vegetarian.

The thing is this: there are things you can do and things you can eat that can *make you feel happier straight away.*

Amazingly, some foods can help you get going to face the day. Some activities give you a major boost – direct to the brain.

When you combine the two – eating and doing certain things – those fed up feelings can disappear (along with spots and even excess weight sometimes).

And it's easy. You just make ten small changes to your daily routine.

Are you ready?

10 SMALL, EASY CHANGES

This way to Small, Easy Change No.1

THE ESCALATOR BUSINESS

Turn your back on lifts and escalators

Exercise is good for you. So good that when you do it, your body says 'thanks' by boosting happy chemicals in your brain.

But who's got the time or money to go to the gym?

Instead, use the stairs rather than the lift or escalator when you're out shopping, at work or at school.

Climbing stairs is one of the best ways there is to get fitter and get that happy stuff into your head. In fact climbing stairs each day for a year is the same as climbing a large mountain. Great view isn't it!

Decide to do it next time you're out. Then decide to keep on doing it and always take the stairs. Your brain will get happier and happier.

While you're climbing the stairs at the shopping centre, here's what to buy…

THE BANANA THING

Monkeys aren't stupid

Did you ever see a depressed chimp?

Not many people know this, but a banana can help produce the same happy chemical in your head as a pill. What's more, they give you a steady supply of energy. And bananas are available off prescription.

Be honest, ways to feel better don't get much easier than this.

1. Eat a banana.

2. That's it. Eat the banana.

One a day is good, and here's a way to make those good feelings even stronger – walk to the shops and use the stairs when you go and buy your bananas.

Small Easy
Change No.3
next

PUT ON YOUR 'WOW' GLASSES

The world is amazing when you really look at it

When was the last time you went outside and really noticed what's there? The wind, the warmth, the cold, the rain, the trees, the flowers, the shops and the sky.

When you stop and think, the world is full of stuff that makes you go 'Wow!'

People who recover from really bad times often say they appreciate things they used to take for granted. So put on your special glasses and see the world for the amazing place it is.

Even better do it with a friend. Go for walks together, talk about good times, and you'll soon get those happy chemicals coursing through your brain.

TEST IT OUT

Use this page to rate your mood before and after your WOW walk.

Use it to discover the effect of your WOW walk on you.

RATE YOUR MOOD (BEFORE YOUR WALK)

| HAPPINESS | | | | | | | | TICK |
| TENSION OR ANXIETY | | | | | | | | TICK |

| HAPPINESS | | | | | | | | TICK |
| TENSION OR ANXIETY | | | | | | | | TICK |

RATE YOUR MOOD (AFTER YOUR WALK)

YOU OLD
SMOOTHIE

Are you fed up with hearing about 5 a day?

Even if you like fruit and vegetables, it's hard to have five portions a day.

Trouble is, you really do need that much fibre. Without it, your system clogs up and you get all sad and sluggish.

So here's a cheat – drink smoothies. They're just mashed up fruit and veg, usually with most of the good stuff left in, and just one glass a day gets you started. Get a blender and make your own to get the variety.

Ready? Walk briskly to the shop, buy the fruit and veg you like. Walk briskly home, mix, mash and enjoy, feel smug.

Got diabetes or watching your weight? Then choose low sugar fruits like berries, cherries, apples, grapefruit, pears, apricots, strawberries, plums and of course bananas (lower sugar when they are under-ripe).

DOING
PORRIDGE

Breakfast gets you going

It's amazing but it's true. When you do without breakfast, your body doesn't get the right kind of start and it sulks all day, demanding coffee or snacks and often giving you a headache by lunchtime.

But when you eat a bowl of porridge or muesli each morning, you don't need all those snacks, your digestion works better and your day gets off to a great start.

Porridge and muesli work like – how can we put this – drain unblockers. After a few days they clear your system out and you feel better all round.

Walk quickly to the corner shop and buy some, now.

HEAVY
BREATHING

Faster, faster

You already exercise. If you do household chores, they're exercise. When you clean the car or do the garden, that's exercise. When you lift or move things at work or school, that's exercise.

So why don't you feel better? Because you're not doing it fast enough. Exercise only works properly and produces happy chemicals when you get out of breath, and your heart starts pumping.

So do the housework faster. Clean the car quicker. Take a brisk walk for 20-30 minutes. Move those files or shift those boxes at a run (always being careful not to take risks or hurt yourself of course).

Oh, and while doing it ...

You could try the next idea

MAKE A NOTE OF THIS

Don't suffer in silence

Music cheers you up. Obvious? So why are you sitting there in silence? Silence is just a space for you to think about your worries in.

Put some of your favourite music on. Do it now. Play music while you're exercising and getting out of breath and it'll send even more happy feelings to your brain.

Play music while you're walking briskly to the shops. Play music while you're sitting around. Create a playlist for when you need a boost.

But don't play sad stuff, or songs that remind you of unhappy times. Keep it upbeat and you'll get an instant lift.

TAKE ONE AWAY

This one saves money too

Eating too much fast food or takeaway food is a great way to get really down.

Did you see that experiment where a man ate nothing but fast food? He felt depressed and really unhealthy inside a couple of weeks.

So here's what you do: cut out one burger or take-away a week. Just one. Replace it with something you make yourself (easy things like beans on toast are fine).

It won't change your life all at once, but put together with the extra exercise and healthier eating you're doing, within a few weeks you'll start to feel lighter, fitter and happier. And a bit better off.

HELP!

It ain't what you do, it's who you do it for

Do a small kindness for someone else, every day, and you'll feel even better than they do. What's more, you'll feel good straight away.

It doesn't have to be a big thing like sometimes helping at a soup kitchen or drop-in centre (although those would be great, of course).

You can just as easily get a lift in your mood by helping someone with their work, writing a letter of thanks for being your friend, cooking a meal or spending time with a person who needs the company.

Go on, sit down now and plan one or two helpful things you're going to do for other people this week. They'll feel good, but you'll feel even better!

Final idea coming up next

THE HAPPY LIST

Remember the good things

When you're down it's easy to forget the good times- times you've succeeded in something, happy times with friends, things that make you smile and times you did something to help someone else.

So remember them. Each evening, sit down and write down three things that you:

- have enjoyed

- felt was a job well done

- or helped you feel close to someone else

Is there anything to be thankful for? After a few days, you'll have a list of great things that you can look back on, and this will help you feel a lot better.

What you think about affects how you feel. Focus on the good things and you'll be happier for it!

Try it out

MY
GOOD
TIMES

Write down all the things you've enjoyed, felt was a job well done, or has helped you feel close to someone else.

How much did it fit with your values/ideals of how you want to live your life? Is there anything to be thankful for?

WHAT ARE YOU WAITING FOR?

Go and get that banana

At the beginning of this book, we promised you could start feeling better in ten minutes. It's time, so here's what to do – make a plan and get going.

Pick one small thing then use the Planner sheet on pages 34/35 to give yourself the best start.

If it's daylight, go out, walk briskly to the corner shop and buy a couple of bananas. Walk quickly home and eat them.

If it's night and the shops are closed, walk up and down your stairs for ten minutes, or long enough to get your heart pumping.

Whichever you do, you'll know you're making changes that make a difference

Once you're done, use the Review sheet on pages 36/37 to check your progress.

Go, make a plan

DON'T JUST SIT THERE, MAKE A PLAN!

1. WHAT AM I GOING TO DO?

2. WHEN AM I GOING TO DO IT?

3. WHAT PROBLEMS OR DIFFICULTIES COULD ARISE, AND HOW CAN I OVERCOME THEM?

DATE

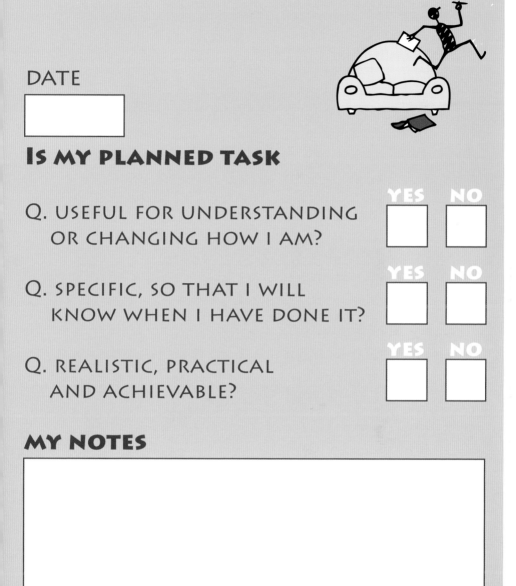

Is my planned task

Q. USEFUL FOR UNDERSTANDING
OR CHANGING HOW I AM?

YES NO
☐   ☐

Q. SPECIFIC, SO THAT I WILL
KNOW WHEN I HAVE DONE IT?

YES NO
☐   ☐

Q. REALISTIC, PRACTICAL
AND ACHIEVABLE?

YES NO
☐   ☐

MY NOTES

OK, HOW DID IT GO?

WHAT DID YOU PLAN TO DO?
WRITE IT HERE

DID YOU TRY TO DO IT?   YES   NO

IF YES:
1. WHAT WENT WELL?

2. WHAT DIDN'T GO SO WELL?

3. WHAT HAVE YOU LEARNED FROM WHAT HAPPENED?

DATE

4. HOW ARE YOU GOING TO APPLY WHAT YOU HAVE LEARNED?

IF NO: WHAT STOPPED YOU?

INTERNAL THINGS
(FORGOT, TOO TIRED, PUT IT OFF, DIDN'T THINK I COULD DO IT, COULDN'T SEE THE POINT ETC.).

EXTERNAL THINGS
(OTHER PEOPLE, WORK OR HOME ISSUES ETC.).

HOW COULD YOU HAVE PLANNED TO TACKLE THESE THINGS?

Do these things regularly, along with the other small, easy changes in this book and you'll be amazed how your mood (and your health) will improve! Go for it!

37

WHERE TO GET EVEN MORE HELP

(but no broccoli)

For more tips on feeling better, go to www.llttf. com. It's free, and it's packed with ways to lift your mood and start having a healthier life.

There are links on there, too, so you can connect with other people who are using food and exercise to feel great.

And don't worry, last time we looked, very few vegetables were mentioned.